ALL ABOUT ME!

Name:

....

....

Age: ....

Birthday:

....

....

My Hobbies:

....

....

....

....

My favourite food:

Draw it! ↗

My favourite music: ....

....

My Favourite Colour:

My Favourite Book:

....

....

....

My best holiday: ....

Why: ....

....

....

What are your hopes and dreams for 2023?

MY 2022!

I'm most proud of doing this in 2022...

....
....
....
....
....
....
....

TRACY BEAKER AWARD

My biggest wish is...

My top read of 2022...

....
....

Something new I want to try in 2023...

....
....
....

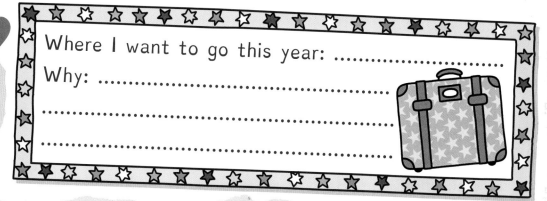

Where I want to go this year: ....
Why: ....
....
....

My 2023 resolutions...

① ....
② ....
③ ....
④ ....

How many books I want to read this year!

JW Shining Stars Awards!

It's THE hottest red carpet event of the year!

LOL ALERT

WINNER – Gemma's Revenge!
Yes, it's super-naughty (and we definitely DON'T recommend you try this at home!) but we couldn't help spluttering with laughter when Gemma splatted snooty Flora in the face with her homemade chocolate cake!
Gemma 1 – Flora 0

CHEEKIEST CHARACTER

A worthy winner, I'm sure you'll agree!

WINNER – Tracy Beaker!
All hail the Queen of Sass, Miss Tracy Beaker!
Marty from *The Worst Thing About My Sister* came pretty close in this category, but Tracy's oh-so-many mischievous antics and naughty pranks definitely deserve the crown!

DRAMA QUEEN

WINNER – Hetty Feather!
Whether she's delighting the crowds at the Calvacade with her penny-farthing stunts, posing as a mermaid for Mr Clarendon's Seaside Curiosities or wowing audiences at Tanglefield's Circus, Hetty is always the centre of attention! Even her fanciful names are spectacularly theatrical!

Which of Hetty's stage names do you like best?
Sapphire Battersea ☐
Emerald Star ☐

OMG MOMENT

WINNER – Vicky's Accident
Talk about an explosive opening! The first chapter of *Vicky Angel* is such an unexpected and totally tragic event it really does rate as one of Jacky's most shocking story twists...

TOTAL TEAR-JERKER

WINNER – Marigold's Breakdown
We shed more than a tear or two when poor Marigold had to be taken to hospital, leaving Dolphin behind. Saddest chapter EVER.

MOST LOVABLE

WINNER – Biscuits
Everyone loves Billy McVitie, AKA Biscuits! This delightfully round fellow pops up in more than one of Jacky's stories – can you name them all?

1. _____
2. _____
3. _____

BIGGEST BADDIE

WINNER – Kim, *Bad Girls*
Lots of Jacky's stories feature a mean girl (Skye, Justine and Rhiannon, to name just a few!) but Kim definitely takes the bad girl crown! Her bullying and taunts really push poor Mandy to the edge... of the pavement, eek!

BEST JW BOOK

WINNER – ???
We couldn't possibly pick just one!
Do YOU have a special favourite?

What would your choices be for each award category?
Fill in your picks below:

LOL Alert _____

Cheekiest Character _____

Drama Queen _____

OMG Moment _____

Total Tear-jerker _____

Most Lovable _____

Biggest Baddie _____

Best JW Book _____

ANSWERS: Biscuits appears in *Best Friends*, *Cliffhanger* and *Buried Alive*.

All About Jacky!

Hello, and welcome to the acqueline Wilson annual 2023! I'm Jacky!

I'm terribly excited for you to get stuck into this annual. You'll meet lots of my favourite characters, from Tracy Beaker to the Runaway Girls!

How many of my books have you read?

Each character even has their own special activities, art and games for you to enjoy.

On the very next page I've answered some questions for you — especially for this annual! — and I'll even let you in on my writing secrets!

Sketch yourself here as a JW character!

Do you have a favourite character from my books? Let me know in the space below...

1 ....
2 ....
3 ....

Jacky Answers All!

Jacky talks reading habits, writing inspiration and reveals her fave bookish snacks!

ALL ABOUT... WRITING!

What is the most random thing that inspired you to write a story?

I think it was when I was doing a long book-signing. Two little girls came up to me hand-in-hand and chorused "Hello, we're Gemma and Alice, and we're best friends." I thought this was so sweet I decided to write a book called *Best Friends* and called the main girls Gemma and Alice.

What's your most important piece of advice for young writers?

I think it's good to read a great deal to see how other writers construct their stories, and also to keep a diary to get into a regular writing habit.

What are your best and worst writing habits?

My best habit is that I write every single morning, sitting up in my bed in my pyjamas. My worst writing habit is that I often lose track of the days in my stories and have a Thursday coming after a weekend or some similar mistake. My copy editors must sigh whenever they have to point this out!

Describe the perfect environment for writing...

Well, I like to write soon after I wake up — but I'm actually happy to write anywhere, at any time. I don't even mind if I'm scribbling on the back of a big envelope or typing on my laptop — just as long as I get the story down! I don't mind background noise. I even hold conversations when I'm typing away.

ALL ABOUT... READING!

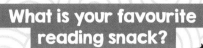

What are your top three favourite books of all time?

It's so hard to choose, but I think I like *Ballet Shoes* by Noel Streatfeild, *I Capture The Castle* by Dodie Smith, and *Jane Eyre* by Charlotte Bronte the most. I've read them all at least five times.

Where is your favourite reading spot?

I have lots — I like to read in bed, or curled up on the sofa, or lounging on a deckchair in the garden, or travelling on a train, or at the kitchen table eating a meal (though this is not good manners!).

What is your favourite reading snack?

I think Jo March in *Little Women* had it sussed — she liked to eat apples, and so do I!

If you could live in any world from a book, where would it be, and why?

Somewhere cosy and safe, like Milly-Molly-Mandy's little cottage in the country.

Do you prefer reading outside on a breezy summer's day or wrapped up warm inside on a cold, snowy day?

I like to do both — though I think I concentrate better indoors.

If you could live the life of one of your characters, who would it be and why?

I think it would be Hetty Feather — she's had a very difficult time in many ways, but she's got such spirit that I think she'll have the most interesting life and make incredible friends.

What is a quote from a book you've read that you will always remember?

I was very pleased when my book *Hetty Feather* was made into a wonderful stage play by Emma Reeves. She has Madame Adeline say to Hetty when she's comforting her "Everything's better with cake". I didn't write this myself, but it's a quote that's stuck in my mind. And it's right, everything *is* better with cake!

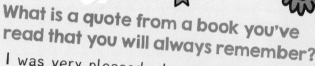

Are you more creative in the morning or at night?

I prefer to write in the morning, but sometimes I might suddenly get an idea when I'm ready for bed and feel compelled to get it written out.

What helps you focus when writing?

It takes a minute or two of concentrating at first, but once my fingers start darting across the keyboard then I'm in my own imaginary world.

What are your biggest dos and don'ts?

Imagine how your characters are feeling and write lots of conversation. Don't get discouraged — try to get to the end of your story and then do some rewriting if you feel you need to.

THE STORY MACHINE!

All of these things add up to make an amazing story!

Either roll a dice or pick a number at random to choose each element of your story!

An awesome character!

1. Nigel McBurty — a crime-fighting penguin keeper who has a love of stinky cheese!
2. Camilla Grenadine — a cruise-loving socialite who is scared of heights!
3. Mathias Argo — a fearless sailor who loves adventure... and stripy socks!
4. Ellen Knutt — a no-nonsense schoolteacher who has a passion for line-dancing!
5. Horace Monkonov III — an extremely rich old man who loves playing tricks on his servants!
6. Make up your own awesome character!

An amazing setting!

1. An old, abandoned boarding school.
2. A glittering theatre on the opening night of a show.
3. A deep, dark forest in the middle of nowhere...
4. An exotic desert island where the sun always shines.
5. A derelict old castle, high on a hillside.
6. Make up your own amazing setting!

A gripping plot!

1. There's a bag of money found in the street!
2. Your character discovers someone else's diary down the back of their bookcase!
3. An abandoned puppy needs your character's help!
4. Your character is planning a surprise party, but the person it's for keeps almost finding out...
5. The most embarrassing thing EVER happens to your character — cringe!
6. Make up your own gripping plot!

12

NOW FILL IN ALL THE PARTS TO PLAN YOUR AMAZING STORY...

A shocking twist!

① Your character's worst enemy threatens to share their biggest secret!

② Your character finds out they have a long-lost twin!

③ Someone steals your character's most prized possession!

④ Your character makes the front-page news because of something they did!

⑤ Your character wins a competition to go on the trip of a lifetime!

⑥ Make up your own shocking twist!

The ending!

① A happy ending.

② A tearjerker ending.

③ A cliffhanger ending.

④ A gripping ending.

⑤ A surprise ending.

⑥ Make up your own ending!

Character

Setting

Plot

Plot twist

Ending

My Writing Secrets!

Be inspired by elements to create your next character!

Lots of my characters are inspired by natural elements or materials. There's Violet, Rose and Marigold, who are named after flowers. Opal, Emerald and twins Ruby and Garnet are all named after gemstones. And Dolphin, Star and Pearl are all named after things found in nature, too!

A character's name can often give us a sense of their identity — violet flowers are a gorgeous deep purple and have lots of frilly petals in layers, which is not too dissimilar to Violet's character. She is rather deep and mysterious — and there are lots of layers to her personality, too!

Opals are milky stones that have vibrant colours underneath their opaque outer layer — quite like Opal herself! Although she appears a regular girl, when she looks deep inside, she finds a sparkling personality and there are lots of different facets to who she is — a daughter, a worker, a friend, a Suffragette...

Now let's create some new nature-inspired characters! The elements earth, air, fire and water should give us some interesting names!

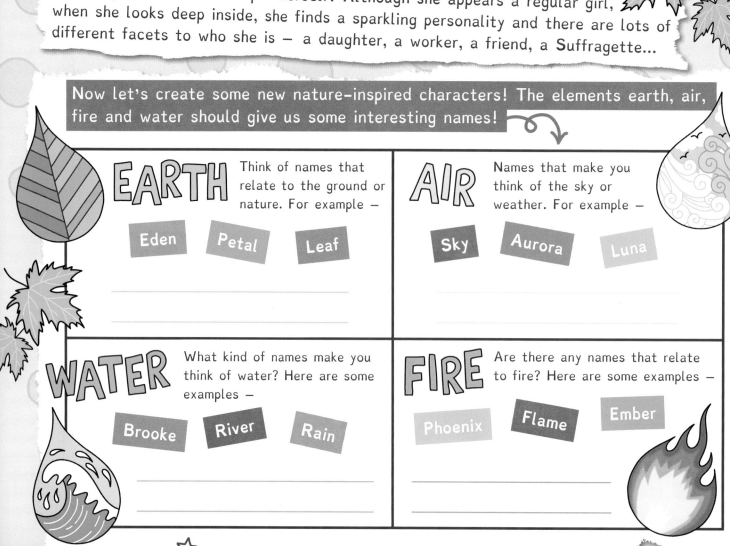

EARTH Think of names that relate to the ground or nature. For example —

Eden   Petal   Leaf

AIR Names that make you think of the sky or weather. For example —

Sky   Aurora   Luna

WATER What kind of names make you think of water? Here are some examples —

Brooke   River   Rain

FIRE Are there any names that relate to fire? Here are some examples —

Phoenix   Flame   Ember

Now think up an interesting surname for your character.

I'm sure you know the story of how I named Tracy Beaker... I was having a bath, and I was looking around for inspiration. I knew I wanted to call my character Tracy, but Tracy Soap? Tracy Flannel? Tracy Toothbrush? I was rinsing my hair with an old beaker I used instead of a shower head and all of a sudden, I thought, "Aha! Tracy Beaker!"

Have a look around and see what inspires you!

I can see...

Write down some ideas here!

- Curtains
- Table
- Chair

....

....

....

....

....

....

Now match your character first name with a surname — Luna Curtain has a certain ring to it, don't you think...?

Luna means moon, so I think Luna Curtain would be a calm, quiet, thoughtful girl, who loved reading and being creative!

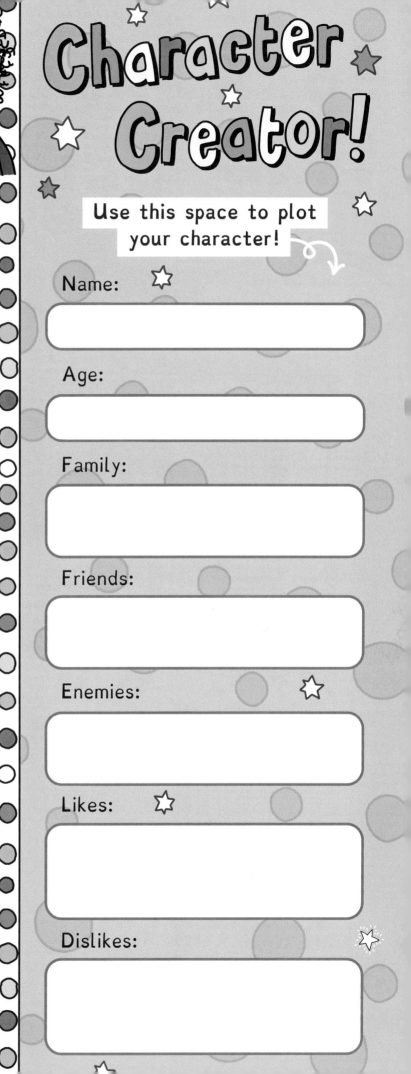

Character Creator!

Use this space to plot your character!

Name:

Age:

Family:

Friends:

Enemies:

Likes:

Dislikes:

Stuck for story ideas? Play along for picture inspiration!

How to play:

1. Roll a dice and match the number to find your first picture choice.

2. Pick a colour from purple, pink, orange, green or blue and match the colour square to find your second picture.

3. Now choose one of these gemstones and match it to get your third and final picture.

4. Got your three pictures? Great! It's time to write a story based around your three picture prompters. It doesn't matter what order you write it in, just as long as you include all three objects. You can make it as serious or as silly as you like!

16

Play again to get three new pictures for your next story!

Tremendous Tracy Beaker

Black belt Tracy

Greetings, adoring fans of the Talented, Tremendous and Terrific Tracy B (that's me, if you didn't already know!).

As you already own this Amazing Annual, I don't suppose I'll need to extol the virtues of the entire thing, but what I will say is this: the next few pages — the Tracy Beaker pages, if you will — are my personal favourites.

You can play my Truth or Dare game, prove you're the biggest Beaker fan ever and find out if you're just like Marvellous Me (Tracy Twins!)! I'll even help you write the Best Ever story and let you give me a colourful makeover! Turn the page to find out more!

Question Time!

Can you answer these questions about Marvellous Moi?

1. What does my mum do for a living?

2. What's the name of my annoying and wobbly-bummed social worker?

3. What's my favourite name in the world ever?

Am I telling Whopping Great Fibs or being Oh-So-Honest? You decide!

Tracy's TRUE or FALSE!

1 Justine-Can't-Keep-Her-Hands-To-Herself-Littlewood broke my Mickey Mouse alarm clock.

Totally Truthful ☐
Beaker Bluff ☐

2 I once went out in the garden Completely and Utterly NAKED!

Totally Truthful ☐
Beaker Bluff ☐

3 Miss Simpkins gave me the part of the Ghost of Christmas Present in our school's play of A Christmas Carol.

Totally Truthful ☐   Beaker Bluff ☐

HURRAY!
THE GREATEST PERFORMANCE EVER!
WELL DONE TRACY!
MAGNIFICENT!
A TRUE STAR IS BORN!

4 The Dumping Ground's pet rabbit is called Cabbage. I'd much prefer a big Rottweiler to scare away my enemies! (That means YOU, Justine-Better-Watch-Out-Littlewood!)

Totally Truthful ☐   Beaker Bluff ☐

5 My dream meal is a strawberry milkshake, Big Mac and fries from McDonald's — yum yum!

Totally Truthful ☐
Beaker Bluff ☐

6 My birthday is on December 8. I expect my mum will shower me with Incredibly Expensive and Tasteful presents!

Totally Truthful ☐
Beaker Bluff ☐

20

Which Dumping Ground Character Are You?

Take our fun quiz to find out!

START

Are you a girlie girl?
— YES →
— NO →

Do you hate it when people touch your things?
— YES ↓
— NO →

Are you outgoing and confident?
— YES
— NO ↓

Do you like looking after other people?
— NO →
— YES →

Do you get angry easily?
— NO →
— YES ↓

You love the colours red and blue!
— YES →
— NO ↓

Do you have just a couple of really close friends?
— NO →
— YES ↓

YOU ARE...

TREMENDOUS LIKE TRACY!
You love writing stories about your crazy life; just like Tracy! You're really independent and can be a teeny bit too bossy sometimes but that's OK because everyone loves your boisterous personality!

CALM LIKE CAM!
Like Cam with Tracy, you're a totally calming force over all your crazy mates! You're always there for your friends and hardly ever get angry. You're kind and caring and all your friends come to you for your brilliant advice!

LOYAL LIKE PETER!
Peter gets on Tracy's nerves most of the time but he's a great friend and fiercely loyal. You're the same way with your best mates and are always looking out for them. You're very level-headed, but don't forget to let yourself have some fun!

MISCHIEF & MAYHEM WORD FINDER!

Step 1: Find all words in grid.
Step 2: Bask in the glory of your amazingness.

```
D J Y P D G H W P W T H W N E
E E S L U V I R A Y R S U O O
Z P S U N L E R N V O I R I K
U O L T O D L N D J U P M T G
S H E A R I P K E G B M N O J
B Q R O Y U C D M B L I Z M G
W W S X B F C I O S E S R M D
D I N B J O U T N B A H N O H
D G F Z V U H L I R W C K C J
V T T A I E C V U O E I A T S
J P H L R L A H M O N P X R S
E M O S C I L O R F H R G U F
X J O X A D T R N A U G H T Y
D M Q H D R A W Y A W D W N A
E D G L B Q F K Z V A C X K I
```

Can you find these words that mean mischievous or mayhem?

BOTHERSOME   IMPISH
COMMOTION   NAUGHTY
DESTRUCTION   PANDEMONIUM
DISORDER   PERNICIOUS
FRACAS   PLAYFUL
FROLICSOME   TROUBLE
HAVOC   WAYWARD

Circle the words that mean mischievous and put a star next to the ones that mean mayhem — now use them in your next story!

ARE YOU A BEAKER EXPERT?

Fill in the gaps with the correct characters to prove you're a Beaker brainbox!

FABULOUS Hetty Feather!

Roll up, roll up — it's time to join me, Hetty Feather, for a fun historical extravaganza! You'll be thrilled, astonished and entertained, I guarantee it!

Gasp and marvel at my best bookish moments, dazzle your friends with your poetry writing skills and solve my particularly puzzling brain busters! Everyone knows that I love being centre stage — my Big Top Pom Poms will help you show off in style! So crafty! Don't forget to take my Victorian quiz!

Love from, Hetty x

VERY Victorian!

Match the last digit from your phone number to find a Victorian character for your next story!

0 — Mabel Bloom
1 — Florence Richmond
2 — Doris Lovat
3 — Kitty Pearce
4 — Winnifred Pill
5 — Ethel Babbage
6 — Opal Larkin
7 — Constance Pratt
8 — Agnes Pegsworth
9 — Myrtle Webb

HETTY'S

We love reading about Hetty's adventures at the Foundling Hospital — these are a few of our favourites...

1

MARVELLOUS JEM!

Hetty has a special place in her heart for her dear foster brother, Jem Cotton — and so do we! We love how he cares for Hetty, especially when he insists on travelling with her back to the Foundling Hospital! Such a lovely, bittersweet moment! Who wouldn't want a special friend like Jem?

2

TANGLEFIELD'S CIRCUS

ROLL UP! ROLL UP!

Hetty's first ever trip to Tanglefield's Travelling Circus was full of wonder! We were just as mesmerised by the clowns and trapeze artists as Hetty and Jem were — and we simply marvelled at the descriptions of stunning Madame Adeline and her pretty performing horses!

3

LOL!

We laughed so hard when naughty Hetty renamed her matrons Matron "Stinking" Bottomly and Matron "Pig-Face" Peters!

Which *Hetty Feather* moments make you LOL? Write them here!

Best Bits!

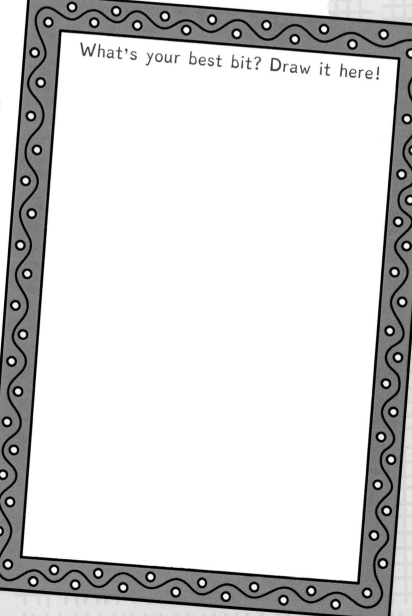

KINDLY IDA!

The Foundling Hospital was full of horror and hardships for poor Hetty, but we were so relieved when she met friendly kitchen-maid, Ida! We just wish our own school lunch ladies would treat us to extra helpings...

5 SENSATIONAL SEQUELS!

Whilst the ending of *Hetty Feather* never fails to put a smile on our faces, we can't help feeling a bit sad that our Hetty adventure is at an end — until we remember that we have four sensational sequels to read next! Yay!

What's your best bit? Draw it here!

How to Write a Poem

I can help you!

A poem is a way to tell a story or say something in a simple and shorter way. It can be about anything you like and it doesn't even have to rhyme!

Think about your subject and write a few notes. Bertie the butcher's boy and Jem both want to write poems for their sweetheart, Hetty, so what do they know about her?

Hetty is feisty and funny. She has sparkling blue eyes and fiery red hair with a temper to match. She's clever and hates being a servant, but loves writing and dreams of becoming a famous author. Most of all, Hetty longs to be known by her real name, Sapphire Battersea.

Bertie ♡s Hetty

Bertie is a cheeky chap and his poem is funny – the second and fourth lines rhyme.

It can help to tap out a rhythm for your words if you want your poem to rhyme. Try something like this —
Da da, da da, da da, da da
Da da, da da, da da

I know a girl called Sapphire
She has eyes of brightest blue
She makes a lovely apple pie
And good steak pudding too

She has some very fancy ways
No servant's life will do
And so I say to Sapphire
I give my heart to you

Try writing your own verse for Bertie's poem here...

_____
_____
_____
_____
_____
_____
_____

o Sapphire with Love

Jem is more serious and hasn't seen Hetty for a long time, so his poem talks about her in a thoughtful and heartfelt way.

Hetty, my friend and sweetheart
How I long to see your face
I recall your sparkling eyes
Your hair of flowing flames
I treasure the letters
    you send to me
I see you touch each page
I close my eyes and dream of you
And whisper your new name
'Sapphire Battersea,
    Sapphire Battersea'
When will we be together?
I'm counting off each day...

Try writing your own verse for Jem's poem here...

_____

_____

_____

_____

_____

WHY NOT?
Pick your fave JW character and write a poem about them!

Acrostic Poems

These are super-simple and super-fun!

An acrostic poem starts with a name or word. The subject of the poem is based on the word you choose. I've written one all about my cat, Jacob. Write down your starting word so it reads vertically, then think about the descriptions you can use, like this

Jumps from branch to branch
Alert and always watching
Curls up cosy by the fireside
Or even better — on my knee
Brings me joy and laughter every day

You might want to write about a favourite event, time of the year, hobby or thing instead —

Crumbly and yummy
All tasty and delicious
Kaleidoscopic sprinkles on top
Especially for me!

Now you try — write one for your best friend here!

Particularly Puzzling

Class Act!

Hetty and Diamond have a new stage for their act — but where? Solve all the puzzles to find out!

Fit the circus acts below into the grid and an important circus person will be revealed in the shaded boxes...

TRAPEZE

LION TAMING

LASSO

FIRE BREATHING

UNICYCLING

ACROBATICS

TRICK RIDING

DIABLO

JUGGLING

TUMBLING

The important circus person is _ _ _ _ _ _ _ _ _ _

Put the 6th letter of this answer in the 2nd building box on the opposite page. Put the 9th letter in the 9th box.

Double Cross!

Cross out the letters that appear three times or more to reveal one of Diamond's circus co-stars!

Diamond's co-star is _ _ _ _ _ _

Put the 2nd letter of this answer into the 4th building box. Put the 4th letter of this answer into the 3rd box.

S	R	M	L	W	S
A	C	B	P	H	B
X	W	L	E	V	C
S	E	H	I	E	X
I	P	L	B	W	I
C	S	X	H	O	P

What's In A Name?

Oh, no! Part of the circus poster advertising the show has worn off... Can you work out Diamond's full performing title from the clues?

My first is in cat, but not in bat,
My second is the first in hid.
My third is the middle of while,
And my fourth is in loud but not proud.
My last is the first of day.

The missing word is   _ _ _ _ _

Put the 1st letter of this answer into the 1st building box. Put the 4th letter of this answer into the 5th box.

Dear Diary...

Hetty is writing in her diary about someone she has met. Can you work out who?

She lives in a house with a little privet hedge, a patch of emerald-green lawn and a bright flowerbed of marigolds and geraniums edged with scallop shells. She's tall and pale and often dresses in extravagant robes.

CLUE: They appear in the book *Sapphire Battersea*.

The person is   _ _ _ _ _ _

_ _ _ _ _ _ _ _

Put the 13th letter of this answer into the 6th building box. Put the 3rd letter of this answer into the 8th box. Put the 2nd letter of this answer into the 7th box.

Hetty and Diamond's new show is at the

BIG TOP POM-POMS

Make show—stopping decorations from old T—shirts!

1.

Draw two circles on the cardboard, each approximately 14cm wide — we drew round a bowl. Draw a smaller circle within each circle — these should be around 6cm wide. Carefully cut them out.

2.

Cut a small wedge from your cardboard templates to create a gap.

Take one strip and sandwich it between the two templates. We used the hem of the T-shirt because it's thicker and stronger.

3.

Lay out your T-shirt and cut strips of around 11/2 cm thick.

4.

Place the other ring on top!

YOU'LL NEED:

★ An old T-shirt

★ Cardboard

★ Scissors

(one T-shirt makes one pom-pom)

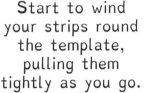

Start to wind your strips round the template, pulling them tightly as you go.

TIP!

Take your scissors and trim your pom-pom to give it a nice, round fluffy shape!

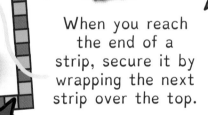

5.

6.

When you reach the end of a strip, secure it by wrapping the next strip over the top.

7.

8.

...eep winding until you have three ...ayers. Carefully take the ends of the sandwiched strip and loosely knot them together to hold your layers in place while you cut.

Very carefully, snip the fabric layers along the side of the template. Use your other hand to hold the strips in place. Gently remove the cardboard templates and pull the sandwiched strings as tight as they will go. Tie in a secure knot to hold your pom-pom together.

VERY VICTORIAN!

Which of these statements about Victorian Britain are true?

Give yourself 1 point for every correct answer.

1. On a particularly sunny day you could take a pleasant dip in the Thames. True ☐ False ☐

2. One would wear a crinoline around the neck. Fabulous! True ☐ False ☐

8. Pig trotters are a delicious street snack. True ☐ False ☐

GULP!

4. Hunting for ferns is THE hottest craze! True ☐ False ☐

5. Conkers is a delightful game to be played in the spring. True ☐ False ☐

6. Breaking news! Queen Victoria will wear black mourning clothes for 10 years! True ☐ False ☐

7. Cleaning the pavement outside your house is the law. True ☐ False ☐

8. Potatoes and rotting vegetables is on the menu every day for the poorest families. True ☐ False ☐

9. A 'chuckaboo' is a super-cute baby. True ☐ False ☐

YOU SCORED...

1–3 Utter codswallop! You'd barely last a week before catching some terrible disease or getting nicked for leaving your doorstep dirty...

4–6 A solid attempt — bravo! It would seem that you have the makings of a rather fine Victorian but there is always more to learn.

7–9 Top marks! Very impressive! You'd take the highs, the lows (and the downright dirty!) parts of Victorian life in your stride.

ANSWERS:
1. False — Only if you wanted to catch a deadly disease... the Thames was thick with sewage, yuck! 2. False — A crinoline was a caged skirt worn under a dress. 3. True 4. True 5. False — Conkers was played in autumn, when the conkers fell from the trees. 6. False — She wore mourning clothes for 40 years! 7. True 8. True 9. False — Chuckaboo was a Victorian word for bestie!

Quality Queenie

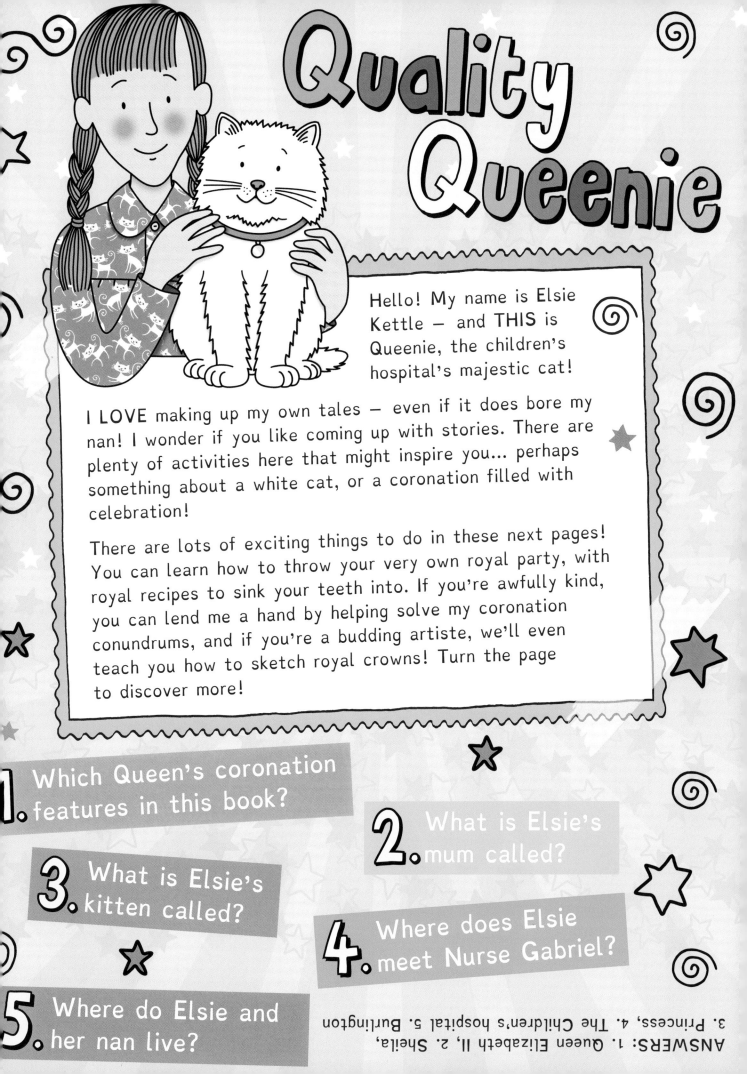

Hello! My name is Elsie Kettle — and **THIS** is Queenie, the children's hospital's majestic cat!

I **LOVE** making up my own tales — even if it does bore my nan! I wonder if you like coming up with stories. There are plenty of activities here that might inspire you... perhaps something about a white cat, or a coronation filled with celebration!

There are lots of exciting things to do in these next pages! You can learn how to throw your very own royal party, with royal recipes to sink your teeth into. If you're awfully kind, you can lend me a hand by helping solve my coronation conundrums, and if you're a budding artiste, we'll even teach you how to sketch royal crowns! Turn the page to discover more!

1. Which Queen's coronation features in this book?

2. What is Elsie's mum called?

3. What is Elsie's kitten called?

4. Where does Elsie meet Nurse Gabriel?

5. Where do Elsie and her nan live?

ANSWERS: 1. Queen Elizabeth II, 2. Sheila, 3. Princess, 4. The Children's hospital 5. Burlington

A ROYAL CELEBRA

When Queen Elizabeth was crowned, there were lots of parties to celebrate — here's how to throw one of your own!

Itsy-bitsy Bunting!

Ask an adult to help!

Pin this pretty bunting to your wall or attach to the edge of a tablecloth!

2. Carefully pierce through each heart as shown using a pin cushion. Make sure you have two holes — one on each side.

1. Cut brightly coloured paper into hearts using this template.

Tiny Toppers!

These cupcake toppers can also be stuck in sandwiches — cute!

3. Fit the two hearts together, then use glue to add a cocktail stick — once dry, pop the toppers in your cake!

1. Use the template to cut hearts from brightly coloured paper.

2. Take two hearts in different colours and cut notches like this.

ION!

3. Use a needle and thread to link the hearts together. Ta-da!

A Royal Recipe!

Coronation chicken was invented in the 1950s — to celebrate Queen Elizabeth's coronation — that's how it got its name!

1. Combine the mayo, curry powder, cinnamon, pepper, chutney and sultanas together and mix well.

You'll Need:
- Cold cooked chicken
- 3tbsp mayonnaise
- 1tsp curry powder
- ½ tsp cinnamon
- Ground black pepper
- 1tbsp mango chutney
- Sultanas or raisins

2. Dice or shred the cold cooked chicken and add it to the sauce, making sure it's well covered.

3. Keep refrigerated until ready to serve — add the chicken to salads, sandwiches, wraps and baked potatoes! Yum!

Tip!
If you don't like chicken, this sauce is super-tasty with grated carrot!

39

Coronation

Elsie's going to the Queen's Coronation — but she's lost her invite! Can you figure out where the ceremony's taking place?

Blyton Besties!

Fit the other patients from Blyton ward into the grid to reveal Elsie's favourite nurse!

RITA

MICHAEL

ANGUS   BABETTE   GILLIAN

MARTIN   MAUREEN

T

R

H

Nurse _ _ _ _ _ _ _

Put the 2nd letter of the answer in the 12th box, the 3rd letter in the 14th box and the 5th letter in the 6th box.

Su-purr Secret!

| 1 | 2 | 3 | 4 | | 5 | 6 | 7 | 8 | 9 |

Elsie pretends the kittens on her chocolate box lid are real! Solve this secret code to discover their names.

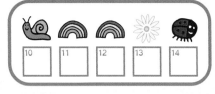

| 10 | 11 | 12 | 13 | 14 |

| 15 | 16 | 17 | 18 | 19 | 20 | 21 | 22 | 23 |

A 🧁 B ⭐ C 🍂 D 🍒 E 🦋 F 🌼 G ☀ H 🍫 I 🍓
J 🐝 K ⚽ L 🥤 M 🦋 N 🐟 O 🌈 P 🍌 Q 🍉 R 👟
S 🐌 T ✳ U 🍊 V 🍍 W ⭐ X 🍎 Y 🐞 Z 🌸

Put 4th letter in the 1st box, the 10th letter in 8th box, the 14th letter in 16th box and the 15th letter in the 5th box.

Conundrum!

Toy Trunk!

Fill in the missing letter on each line to make two new words. The name of Elsie's toy elephant will appear in the boxes.

OPER ☐ PPLE

TAL ☐ IGHT

GRA ☐ ERRY

TIM ☐ CLIPSE

CARRIE ☐ OYAL

HEAR ☐ OWER

Put the 3rd letter in the 13th box, the 4th letter in the 10th box, the 5th letter in the 11th box and the last letter in the 9th box.

Pet Puzzler!

Elsie is given one of Queenie's kittens as a pet. What did she call it?

A) Duchess
B) Princess
C) Countess

Put the 4th letter of the answer in the 7th answer box and the 8th letter in the 3rd answer box.

Silly Surname!

Cross out the letters that appear three times to reveal Nan's and Elsie's surname.

BAKEBTATLEBA

Put the 2nd letter in the 2nd box, the 3rd letter in the 4th box and the last letter in the 15th box.

The Coronation will take place in:

1	2	3	4	5	6	7	8	9	10	11

12	13	14	15	16

41

How To Draw: CROWNS!

This cute crown is sooo easy to draw!

1.

2.

3.

4.

Draw your crown in this box.

Colour in these crowns your way!

Cute Cookie

Hello, my name's **Beauty Cookson**, but I HATE being called that!
I much prefer the nickname Mum gave me — Cookie! Everyone likes
a cookie, right?

Do you like to draw? Perhaps you'll enjoy drawing me — turn the page
for a step-by-step guide!

You can probably tell from my name that I love to bake! I hope you
like my cookie recipe — solve some fun puzzles to find some mystery
mix-ins to make them extra-special! Plus, there are loads of doughnut
delights to try out and some sweet burrowing bunnies — guaranteed
to put a smile on your face!

Love from,
Cookie x

If You're Bored...

Customise some old clothes. ☐

Give your room a makeover! ☐

Make a collage from old magazines. ☐

Plan a picnic or sleepover! ☐

Design your own birthday cards! ☐

Paint your nails in sweet shades! ☐

Hold a silly selfie contest! ☐

Start a book club! ☐

Write a short story. ☐

Invent a new snack! ☐

How To Draw * Beauty

Sketch Beauty and her new hairdo in four easy steps!

1. Start your sketch of Beauty with a large upside down U shape for her hair. Add the curve of her chin — it's slightly higher at one side — and the two short lines of her neck. Create a collar for Beauty's top with another two curves and join them at the sides.

2. Draw in the lines for the fringe of Beauty's new hairstyle. Add longer lines tapering inward as you come down each side of her face. Draw two curves for Beauty's shoulders and add straight lines to form the sleeves of her top.

Nick's Tip!

Beauty loves her flattering new hairdo, so try some other styles on her too. How would she look with Tracy B's wild, black curls?

3. Next draw Beauty's nose — it's like an upside down 7 — then sketch in the frames of her glasses. Finish adding the lines of her hair and extend her arms below the T-shirt sleeves.

4. Copy this picture to complete Beauty's facial features — she has a pretty smile with dimples on her cheeks and chin. Sketching high eyebrows makes her look even more happy and excited. Add the stripes on her T-shirt and colour her in — Beauty has light brown hair and rosy cheeks.

Why not draw Beauty
at her beloved Rabbit Cove?

Cookie's Mystery Mix-ins!

Classic Cookies!

Make these delicious chocolate chip cookies — they're just begging to be customised by my secret ingredients!

Turn cookies from drab to fab with my mystery ingredients!

You'll need:

- 225g caster sugar
- 200g butter, softened
- 1 egg
- 1tsp vanilla extract
- 300g plain flour, sifted
- 1tsp of baking powder
- A pinch of salt
- 200g chocolate chips

1 Preheat your oven to 160°C/320°F/gas 3 and line a baking sheet with baking parchment.

2 Beat the butter and sugar in a bowl until creamy. Mix in the vanilla extract and beat in the egg.

3 Sieve the flour, baking powder and salt over the mixture and fold in with a wooden spoon.

4 Stir in the chocolate chips, plus a secret ingredient from the page opposite!

5 Scoop out a spoonful of mixture and place on to the baking tray — we used an ice cream scoop! Bake in a hot oven for 8–10 minutes until golden brown.

Always ask an adult to help in the kitchen!

46

Shhh, it's a secret!

Mystery Mix-ins!

Solve these puzzles to find some secret ingredients to add to your cookie batter! Yum, yum!

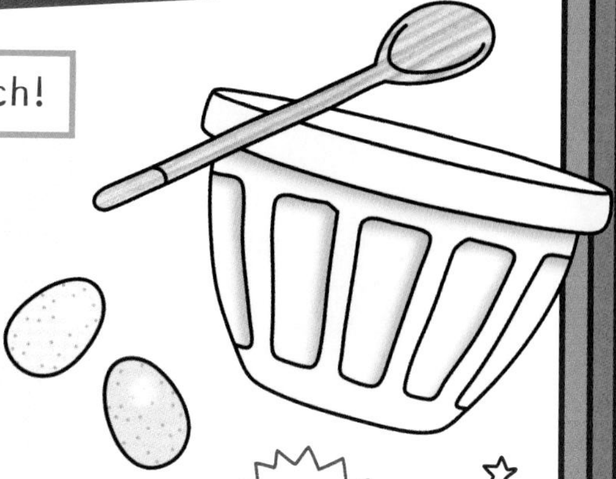

1

This will give your cookies an extra crunch!

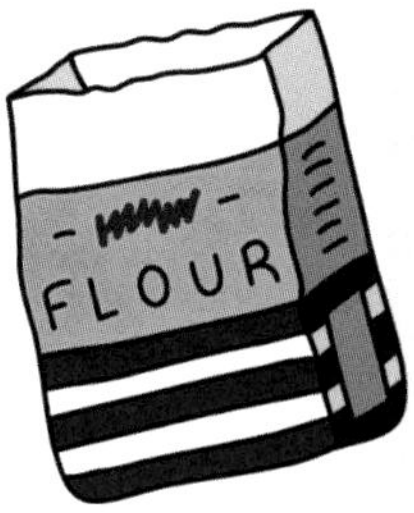

My first is in cake but not in bake,
My second is the last in pipe.
My third is the first in royal,
My fourth is the third in oven.
My fifth is in batter, but not in butter,
My last is the second in blend.

Add 1 handful

Secret Ingredient: ______________________

2

Score out every second letter to add a pinch of this sweet spice!

CDIENTNLAEMBOSNL

Add 1tsp

Secret Ingredient: ______________________

3

Put these words in the grid and the shaded area will reveal all!

MELT **CHOCOLATE**

SUGAR **POWDER**

BEAT

SPOON

Add 2tbsp

Secret Ingredient: ______________________

ANSWERS: 1. CEREAL, 2. CINNAMON, 3. SWEETS.

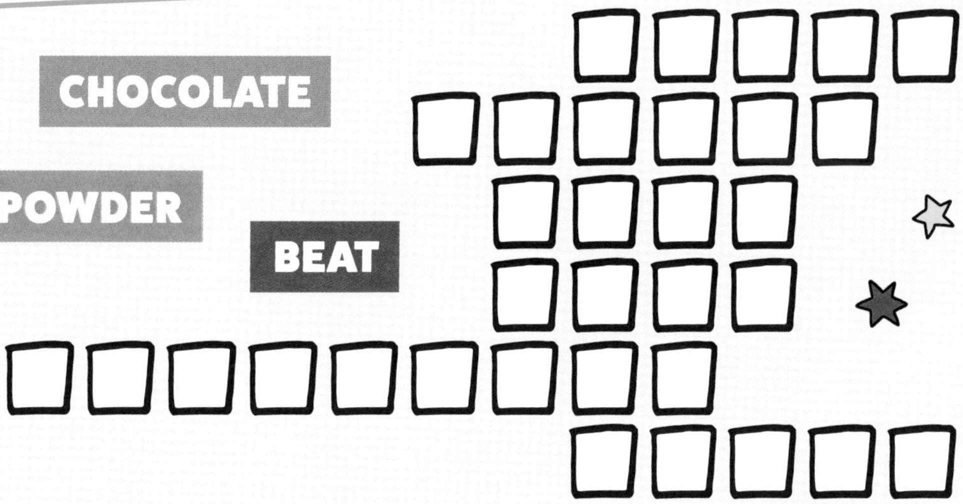

Cookie & Biscuits' Doughnut Delights!

You'll love our delicious doughnut ideas!

National Doughnut Week May 7 – May 15!

Gorgeous Glaze!

Add a few teaspoons of milk or hot water to icing sugar and mix until smooth. Dunk doughnuts in the glaze or spoon it over and let it dribble down the sides!

Cookies and Cream!

Add two tablespoons of cream cheese and a drop of vanilla extract to the glaze and cream together. Crush up some Oreo cookies for the topping.

Minty Fresh!

Add a few drops of peppermint extract and green food colouring to the glaze and dunk the doughnut. Drizzle over melted dark chocolate to finish.

Berry Bites!

Crush and sieve some berries and add the juice to the plain glaze. Cover the doughnuts and sprinkle with some desiccated coconut — berry nice!

Lemon Drizzle!

Add lemon juice and yellow food colouring to the plain glaze. Cover the doughnut and leave it to dry. Drizzle over more icing to decorate.

Tongue Tingler!

Swap water for some sour cream and a little lime juice in the icing mix, and dunk the doughnut. Decorate with popping candy sprinkles — sweet 'n' sour!

48

Salted Caramel Delight!

Add caramel sauce, cocoa powder and a pinch of salt to the glaze and cover the doughnut. Once dry, drizzle over melted white chocolate. Nom!

Orange Blast!

Swap water for orange juice in the icing mix and add a few drops of orange food colouring. Top with sweet sprinkles.

Choco Nut!

Make chocolate icing by adding some cocoa powder to the plain mix. Dunk the doughnut and sprinkle over some chopped nuts.

Melty Mallow!

Add some marshmallow fluff to the glaze and mix until smooth and spreadable, then ice the doughnut. Drizzle with strawberry syrup and cover with sprinkles!

Design A Doughnut!

Create your own lip-smacking flavours!

What ingredients would you add to make it oh-so delicious?

1. _____

2. _____

3. _____

① ② ③

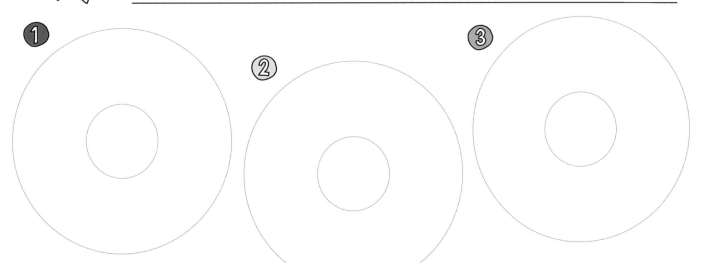

49

Make these funny bunny biscuits – I'll show you how!

MAKE BURROWING BUNNIES!

You'll need:

- Your favourite cookie dough mix
- Pink and white icing
- Mini marshmallows
- Baking paper to line your tray
- Sprinkles to decorate

We used pink and white icing, but why not come up with your own colour combinations?!

1. Roll out the dough to around ½ cm thick, cut out some circles and place them on a lined baking tray.

2. Make feet from dough scraps. Roll a piece into a little ball and flatten into an oval. You'll need two for each cookie.

Tip! Roll your dough between two pieces of baking paper. This will stop it sticking to the rolling pin or table top!

3. Bake all the shapes in the oven for around 10–12 minutes until a light golden brown, following your recipe's instructions. Remove from the oven and leave on the tray to cool.

Ask an adult for help when using the oven!

You could add some jelly beans to the top for bunny ears!

4. Now ice the big circles pink and the smaller ones white. Place two of the white ovals on top of the pink ones to make your bunny bottoms and feet!

5. Add a mini marshmallow for a fluffy bunny tail, and use cake sprinkles to make the details on the feet. A little icing will help them stick. All done – now it's time to eat them! Deeelicious!

50

Terrific Tina!

Hello, and welcome to The Butterfly Club! My name's Tina — I'm a triplet and I'm seven years old. I love butterflies because they are small and delicate, just like me. Turn over the page to read all about The Butterfly Club rules, and then take the quiz to find out who your Butterfly Club triplet is!

Love, Tina x

CREATE YOUR OWN CLUB

★ Club den: ....

★ Meeting day: ....

Where does your club meet? Describe it here! Is it your favourite place, or will you make one up?

What day of the week does your club meet on? Is it at the weekend, one morning before school, or during breaktime?

What password do club members need to get in? Write it upside-down or backwards in case anyone peeks!

★ Club snack:

★ Secret password:

....

What is your club's signature snack? Draw it!

Turn over for more club fun!

CLUB RULES!
Maddie's Mini Quiz!

Let Tina, Phil and Maddie show you how to set up your own club!

What sort of club should you start?

My fave school subject is:
A) Drama ☐
B) English ☐
C) P.E. ☐

When I grow up, I most want to:
A) Win a gold medal! ☐
B) Be a famous pop star! ☐
C) Write a best-selling novel! ☐

Pick the character you're drawn to:
A) Rosalind ☐
B) Destiny ☐
C) Katy ☐

At the weekend I like to:
A) Play lip-sync battle with my mates ☐
B) Head to the park for some fun ☐
C) Curl up with a good book ☐

In class I:
A) Pay attention to my teacher ☐
B) Hum along to my favourite song ☐
C) Play noughts & crosses with my friend ☐

You should start a...

Mostly pink:
Book Club!

Mostly blue:
Music Club!

Mostly green:
Sporty Club!

Tina's Top Tips!

Invite your friends — you could ask your BFFs, classmates or family members.

Design a cool poster or flyer to put up at school!

Think of a fun, safe place to meet!
Take turns in your homes ☐
In the school playground ☐
At the park ☐
In the library ☐
In a classroom ☐
At your local youth club ☐

Hold regular meetings — and keep everyone informed if there's a change!

Take turns bringing snacks for the group!

Plan ahead what you're going to do at your next club meeting!

Don't be bossy — let members vote on important club matters!

Respect everyone's opinion and always be kind!

Ask an adult to help!

Phil's Club Creator!

Fill in the details about your club!

Club Name:

Club Rules

1. ....
2. ....
3. ....
4. ....
5. ....

We aim to: ....
....

Invite people to join and write their names here!

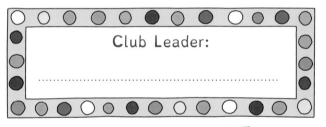

Club Leader:
....

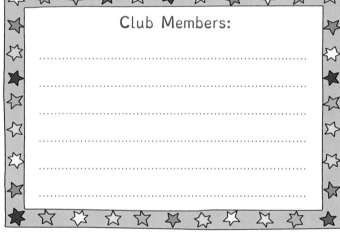

Club Members:
....
....
....
....
....

Design a cool club logo!

Make badges for members!

IS AN OFFICIAL MEMBER OF

My club rules!

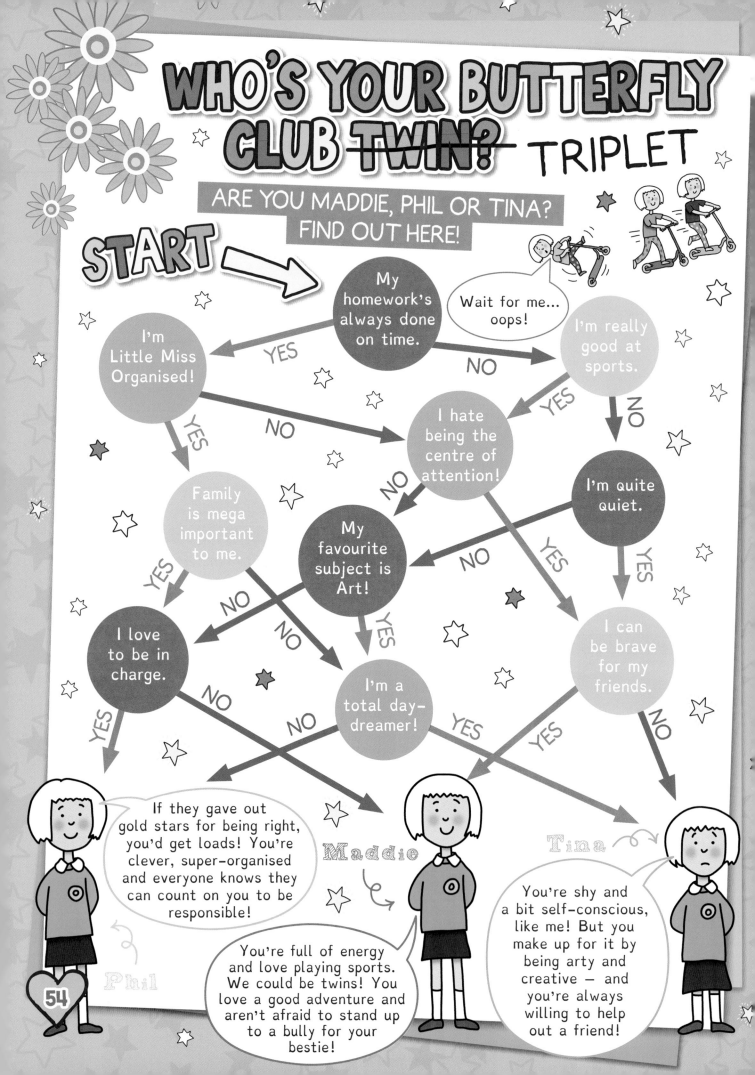

Dazzling Little Darlings!

Hi Everyone,

We're Destiny and Sunset — superstar sisters extraordinaire!
Destiny is an amazing singer and Sunset's a superb songwriter, so
together we're setting our sights on stardom, just like our dad,
Danny Kilman — you've heard of him, right?!
Turn the page to write a celeb-filled showbiz story, then plan the
ultimate show-stopping party with our fab party planner!

Don't forget to write a song with Sunset — it might just be the
next top tune on everyone's lips!

Love, Destiny and Sunset xx

Come join us for star-studded fun
and games! Colour the Hollywood
stars as you complete each activity...

Write a star news story!

Plan the perfect party!

Write a toe-tapping tune!

ooking for more VIP fun? Why not try these fun celebrity
hallenges with your besties...

Dress up in your glitziest clothes and put on a fashion
show in your bedroom! Don't forget to take plenty of
photos!

Act out a scene from a movie and film it on your smartphone.

Pick a dramatic scene from your favourite JW book and read it
aloud as if you're auditioning for a Broadway play!

Jacqueline Wilson

LITTLE
DARLINGS

TWO VERY DIFFERENT GIRLS
ONE EXTRAORDINARY
FRIENDSHIP!

DESTINY   SUNSET

My Writing Secrets!

STORY SCHOOL JW JW

Let's create a showbiz news story together!

Sunset is used to the paparazzi hanging round her house, clamouring desperately in a bid to take a sneaky snap of her famous mum and dad. Flick through any gossip magazine and you'll see pictures and stories of famous people who have been photographed just like Danny and Suzy... they might be all dressed up in a fabulous frock at some swanky awards ceremony, lounging by the pool in a paradise location or simply popping out for some milk!

Follow my tips and bring your feature to life!

First, choose your favourite celebrity to write about and jot down their name. It might be a pop star, sportsperson, an actor – or even me!

....
....
....
....
....

Now think about an amazing news story for your chosen celebrity.

Let's turn everything upside-down and think of a funny situation you would never expect to see your celebrity in... For example, you could say that the famous pop star Ariana Grande was spotted at your local Tesco buying two trolleys full of tins of baked beans! Why was she buying beans? Is she stocking up on them to take back home to her swanky LA pad and introduce them to her American pals, or is she planning on beating the world record for making the tallest-ever stack of beans on toast?

Or, how about this...
The paparazzi have snapped a photo of me wearing an odd floppy hat, pulled right down to hide my hair. Have I dyed my hair a shocking bright pink, or had it cut into a Mohican style?! Perhaps you have a scoop about Danny Kilman?

Whatever you decide to write, keep it light and friendly!

....
....
....

Jacky's Hair 'Mare!

inally, think of
great headline
or your story.

....

A good headline
hould be short
nd snappy —
enough to grab
he reader's
attention. Here
are a few I've
thought up:

ARIANA CANNED-E?

Hat's Going On?

What does it BEAN?

What headlines have you thought up for your
fictional celebrity news story?

....

....

What's Your Diva Rating?

Pick four statements
that sound most like
you to find out!

☐ I'm late for everything

☐ I don't mind getting
my hands dirty

☐ I love posing for photos

☐ I help my mum with
the housework

☐ I spend hours choosing
the perfect outfit

☐ My friends tell me all
their secrets

☐ Accessories are
s-o-o-o essential

☐ I don't like to be the
centre of attention

Mostly pink:

So Sparkly Showbiz!

> I love
> glitz and
> glamour too!

Mostly purple:

Down-to-earth Darling!

> Just like
> me!

Fab Party Planner!

Follow the flowchart to find your perfect party style!

START
I'd love my party to have a theme.

NO → I'm really laid-back.

YES → I love going to the cinema!

I'm really laid-back.
YES → I'd only want my besties to come.
NO → Truth Or Dare is sooo much fun!

I love going to the cinema!
NO → Truth Or Dare is sooo much fun!
YES → I'd like my party to be glam.

Truth Or Dare is sooo much fun!
YES → I'd only want my besties to come.
NO → I'm quite girly.

I'd only want my besties to come.
YES → I love wearing my PJs.
NO → I'm quite girly.

I'd like my party to be glam.
NO → I'm quite girly.
YES → I love celebs.

I love wearing my PJs.
YES → I love being outdoors.
NO → I'd rather be comfy than dress up.

I'm quite girly.
NO → I love celebs.
YES → I'd rather be comfy than dress up.

I love celebs.
NO → I'd rather be comfy than dress up.
YES → The weather forecast is sunny for my party.

I love being outdoors.
YES → GARDEN
NO → SLEEPOVER

I'd rather be comfy than dress up.
YES → GARDEN
NO → MOVIES

The weather forecast is sunny for my party.
YES → GARDEN
NO → MOVIES

SLEEPOVER   GARDEN   MOVIES

58

SLEEPOVER!

- Snuggle down in your room with your besties!

- Ask everyone to bring their comfiest PJs to wear and get changed as soon as everyone arrives!

- Ask your guests to write down a truth and a dare on two separate pieces of paper, then put these in separate bowls — perfect for a game of Truth Or Dare later in the evening!

- Have fun chatting, playing games or watching your favourite movies — the choice is yours!

SERVE:
Pizza (guests can decorate their own if you buy ready-made bases!)
Crisps
Fruit and yoghurt dips
Sweets
Cupcakes (make a decorating station with loads of icing and sprinkles!)
Hot chocolate
Pancakes (for the morning after!)

TOP TIPS!

Follow these to make sure your party goes to plan!

59

Give your friends as much notice as possible when you send or hand out your invites, otherwise they might already have plans!

Make a checklist of all the things you'll need to do or buy before the main event — tick them off as you go!

Create a playlist of your favourite tunes to listen to.

Have some dishes of nibbles set out for your friends to munch on as they arrive!

Most importantly, have fun! It's your party, and it's going to be fabulous!

GARDEN PARTY!

- Go outdoors and have some fun in the sun!

- Prepare some fun outdoor games to keep people occupied — rounders is great if you have a big group of people!

- Decorate an area to sit in — maybe you could put up a tent and fill it with blankets and fairy lights?

- Don't forget the sun-tan lotion if it's going to be a sunny day — no one wants to get sunburn!

SERVE:
Burgers
Hotdogs
Fruit punch (just mix fruit juice with lemonade and add plenty of ice!)
Fruit kebabs
Ice lollies
Ice cream in cones or cups

MOVIE PARTY!

- Grab your favourite films and get ready for a movie party!

- Tell everyone to dress in their most fabulous outfit and pretend you're all movie stars at a posh film premiere!

- Ask guests to bring favourite films and watch them in a movie marathon with the lights turned down!

- Before everyone comes round, write down loads of film titles on strips of paper and put them in a bowl — take turns to pick one and act it out for a fun game of Charades!

SERVE:
Popcorn
Sweets
Cupcakes
Mini hotdogs in rolls
Nachos
Ice cream

Sweets

SONGWRITING with Sunset!

Help me finish my song!

What to do:
Sunset is writing a song for Destiny to perform, but she needs some help to finish it. Now's your chance to collaborate with her! So cool! Just choose a style and fill in the blanks in the lyrics below.

Song Style!

Soft sweet ballad or pure punk rock?! Tick the boxes to decide how your song will sound!

Pick a genre:
- [ ] Pop
- [ ] Rock
- [ ] Hip-hop

Pick a mood:
- [ ] Upbeat
- [ ] Mellow
- [ ] Sad

Choose an instrument:
- [ ] Piano
- [ ] Guitar
- [ ] DJ Deck

Word bank:

Pick from these words to fill in the blanks or think up your own!

Blank 1: Life, school, family, home, teachers, crushes

Blank 2: Failing, cringing, losing, crying

Blank 3: Smiling, laughing, dancing, grinning, giggling, singing

Blank 4: Count, call, lean, fall, rely, depend

Blank 5: Blue, through, cuckoo, eighty-two

Blank 6: Alone, laughing, dancing, smiling

Blank 7: BFFs, best of friends, besties, good friends

Friends Forever
by Sunset and ....

Sometimes .... can get you down
And it's like you're always ....
But you know you'll always have me there
To make you feel like ....

'Cause I know I can .... on you
To be there when I'm ....,
When we're both .... together
Ooh yeah, there's nothing we can't do!

So, I hope we'll stick together,
Be best friends forever and ever,
Ooh .... I know we'll be,
Oh yeah, ... forever!

Why not add more verses? Then can practise perform it your BFF

60

Original Opal!

Dear reader,

My name is Opal Plumstead. I'm just fourteen years old, and I've already been a schoolgirl, a factory worker at Fairy Glen's... and a suffragette!

I adore art, and I'm ever so excited to share some creative activities for you to get stuck into. I'll show you how you can create your very own custom notebook, and even learn to draw Billy the budgie!

I so hope you enjoy these pages — I think they'll be terribly fun!

Shall we get started? Turn over the page!

OPAL'S TRIVIA

1. What is the name of the sweet factory Opal works at?

2. What school did Opal attend?

3. What war is featured in this book?

4. How old is Opal?

5. What is the name of Ms. Robert's son?

ANSWERS: 1. Fairy Glen, 2. St Margaret's school, 3. First World War, 4. Fourteen, 5. Morgan

The Life and Times of
OPAL PLUMSTEAD

Olivia
Opal's BFF

Meet Opal!

Age: 14

Hobbies: Sketching and painting.

School: Star student who won a scholarship!

Opal's story takes place during the Edwardian era — named after King Edward VII. The Edwardian period lasted just nine years, from 1901–1910.

They enjoy:
- Meeting up after school.
- Scoffing Fairy Glen toffees.
- Sharing secrets

In those days, young girls and boys were often employed by factories. In fact, many working children would have been even younger than 14-year-old Opal!

Fairy Glen Factory

Opal's life is turned upside-down when she finds herself working at the local sweet factory!

Mrs Roberts

Job: Owner of Fairy Glen.

Social status: Wealthy upper-class lady.

Interests: Women's rights and the Suffragettes.

Mrs Pankhurst

Mrs Roberts takes Opal under her wing and invites her along to her very first Suffragette meeting.

The Suffragettes were a group of women who fought for the right to vote.

Emmeline Pankhurst passionately believed in the Suffragette motto, 'Deeds not words'. This landed her in trouble when she was sentenced to three months in prison for her part in a violent Suffragette demonstration.

The colours worn by the Suffragettes each had a special meaning.
White: For Purity.
Purple: For Dignity.
Green: For Hope.

Opal and Mrs Roberts feel very honoured to meet Mrs Pankhurst, a very famous Women's Rights Activist.

Mrs Roberts invites Opal to join her for lunch, where she meets Morg — Mrs Roberts' son — for the very first time

VOTES FOR WOMEN

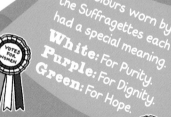

Father
Job: Clerk.
A quiet man who writes books in his free time.

Family!

Primrose Villa
This is where Opal lives. It's a typical Edwardian house made from red brick with a small garden, parlour, living room, kitchen, two bedrooms and a tiny box room — Opal's room!

Mother
Job: Housewife.
A stern woman with a soft spot for her eldest daughter, Cassie.

Cassie
Job: Milliner's apprentice.
Opal's beautiful older sister.

If you were found guilty of a crime in Edwardian times, you would most likely be punished with Hard Labour — this could be anything from building roads to labouring in quarries or on the docks.

Tragedy strikes!
Poor Father finds himself in court! What will become of him if he is found guilty?

Meet Billy!

Happy Days!
Things are looking up for the Plumstead family! Good news means lots of presents — and a new pet!

Songbirds were popular pets of the Edwardians. They were often kept in beautifully ornate cages made from iron — very decorative indeed!

New Friends

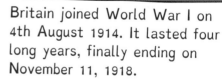

Britain joined World War I on 4th August 1914. It lasted four long years, finally ending on November 11, 1918.
- What will become of Opal?
- Will she ever find happiness?
- What does war mean for Opal, her family and Fairy Glen?

Morgan and Opal get along famously. Could this be true love...?

Just when life is finally falling into place, terrible news threatens to rock Opal's world once again. Britain is at war!

Did you know that Opal Plumstead was Jacky's 100th book? How many of Jacky's books have you read?

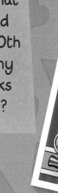

Custom Creations!

EASY

CREATE A TRACY BEAKER DESIGN WITH SOME COLOURED PENCILS OR PENS!

1. Stick a piece of white card to the front of your notebook and start sketching your character in pencil.

2. Go over your design in pen and rub out any pencil lines.

3. Colour in your character — we drew Tracy big on our notebook, so her hair goes right to the edge and gives a bold effect.

MEDIUM

USE OLD COPIES OF *JW MAG* TO MAKE THIS CUTE, QUIRKY DESIGN!

1. Start by making a textured sky with torn tissue paper, then cut pictures from magazines to create a wavy grass shape and the circular sun.

2. Next, add some cutouts from old issues of *JW Mag*. To create a 3D effect, stick some of your cutouts to card and cut out, then stick them to your notebook with sticky foam pads.

3. Finally, add some finishing touches — cotton wool makes perfect wispy clouds and gems and sequins add a bit of sparkle! Use some stickers to add cute elements to the background!

TRICKY

WITH A LITTLE TIME YOU CAN PERFECT THIS AWESOME OPAL DESIGN!

1. Cover your notebook in some pretty paper — we chose crinkly gold tissue paper to give an antique look.

2. Stick the Opal artwork on the opposite page onto card and cut out. Use foam pads to stick the budgie on top of the picture of Opal and the budgie, then stick this to the third picture — this will give a 3D effect. Glue the artwork to the front of your notebook.

3. Now add a title — we wrote My Journal in fancy letters, then cut them out and stuck them down, but you could always use letters cut from magazines.

WHY NOT?
Photocopy a drawing or picture and make up your own 3D art!

How To Draw Billy The Budgie!

Chirp, chirp! Draw Opal's pet budgie in four simple steps...

1. Let's start with Billy's head: sketch an upturned U with a wavy line at the bottom. Now add the details of Billy's beak.

2. Draw a long curved line for his back, one for his wing, and another for his chest. Don't forget to add Billy's foot!

3. Draw Billy's second foot and a long tail with a jagged end. Finally, add a large black dot to create a beady eye.

4. Use a black pen or fineliner and carefully copy this picture, filling in the pattern on Billy's feathers. Use your brightest colours to create an eye-catching plumage!

Have fun drawing lots of budgies with different markings and colours! Take a peek online, or flick through a bird book for inspiration.

Very Violet!

Hello... I'm Violet! If you're looking for magic, fairies and fun, you're in the right place. Find your fairy name, design some fluttery fairies and make the most adorable teeny, tiny toadstools for your garden!

I love making fairies and giving them their own quirks and personalities. Give these fairies below their own profiles!

Name
Favourite colour
Magic power
Lives in
Eats
Lucky charm

Name
Favourite colour
Magic power
Lives in
Eats
Lucky charm

Name
Favourite colour
Magic power
Lives in
Eats
Lucky charm

Name
Favourite colour
Magic power
Lives in
Eats
Lucky charm

CREATE YOUR OWN FAIRY!

You've read all about Violet's fairies... now it's time to create one of your own!

START
Tick four of your favourite pictures to find your fairy type!

Mostly Green
Your fairy is a pretty woodland pixie. They can often be found lounging around on toadstools — but they don't like it when woodland animals disturb their naps. You'll also see them fluttering around trees in the evenings.

Mostly Pink
Flower fairies are very creative, and you might find them painting colours on the wings of passing butterflies. You'll also hear them singing to the flowers early in the mornings — their voice helps them to grow!

Mostly Blue
Water nymphs like to dance on water lilies on the surface of ponds and lakes — you might catch them looking at their reflections in the water too! You'll also see them drying their wings in the sunlight after they've had a swim.

68

FAIRY MAGIC!

Roll a dice to find your fairy's special magical talent.

1 Can speak to all animals and birds

2 Able to travel through time

3 Sprinkling feel-good magic fairy dust

4 Being able to light up the darkest night

5 Singing to make the sun come out

6 Able to breathe underwater

Create Her Personality!

Choose the phrases that sound most like you then count out your score!

- [ ] I'm the loudest of all my friends! **3**
- [ ] I'm always reading! **1**
- [ ] I'm always giggling about something **2**
- [ ] I make new friends easily **3**
- [ ] I can't keep a secret **2**
- [ ] I don't always reply to texts **1**
- [ ] I'm confident about speaking in class **3**
- [ ] I love to play pranks on people **2**
- [ ] Art is my best subject at school! **1**

1-6: Clever Creative

Your fairy is...
- ☆ Super-smart
- ☆ Artistic
- ★ Shy and secretive

7-12: Mischief Maker

Your fairy is...
- ☆ Fun to be around
- ☆ A bit cheeky
- ★ Bubbly

13-18: Cheeky Chatterbox

Your fairy is...
- ☆ Friendly and sociable
- ☆ Confident
- ★ Chatty

Draw your fairy here!

Now you can write a story about your fairy. Have fun!

FAIRY NAME FINDER!

If you were a fairy, what would you be called?

My birth month is:

- ☐ Jan – Moss
- ☐ Feb – Marigold
- ☐ Mar – Flora
- ☐ Apr – Opal
- ☐ May – Glimmer
- ☐ Jun – Dandelion
- ☐ Jul – Luna
- ☐ Aug – Petal
- ☐ Sept – Poppy
- ☐ Oct – Hazel
- ☐ Nov – Blaze
- ☐ Dec – Twinkle

My favourite colour is:

- ☐ Pink – Riverbed
- ☐ Purple – Thistledown
- ☐ Yellow – Windsnap
- ☐ Green – Peppermint
- ☐ Blue – Dewdrop
- ☐ Orange – Shimmerling
- ☐ Red – Rosebud
- ☐ Silver – Moonbeam
- ☐ Gold – Darkling
- ☐ Aquamarine – Evergreen
- ☐ Coral – Starlight

My fairy name is:

....

Why not use this game to make up fairy names for the fairy you created on the last page?

My name would be Glimmer Rosebud!

70

Fluttering Fairies

Design and colour Violet's fairy friends!

Why Don't You...

Put fabulous flowers in their hair?

Design some gorgeous rainbow dresses?

Add some glitter sparkle?

Stick on sequins and gems?

Use scraps of fabric or coloured paper?

Create shimmering fairy jewellery?

Make Teeny Little Toadstools!

The fairies in your garden will love to sit on these!

1. Wash the pebbles in warm soapy water and dry them off. Next paint them red — add two or three coats so they're fully covered.

2. Add the white spots. You can draw these on in pencil first if you like.

The card needs to be thick enough to support the pebbles — so look for something chunky and corrugated.

3. Cut out a strip of card that's 3cm long. Paint it white and leave to dry, then roll into tubes and secure with tape. Snip the tubes so they're all slightly different heights and then tape the pebbles on top.

4. Decorate your toadstools with this cut-out-and-keep fairy. Stick onto cardboard first to make her extra sturdy. You can also draw your own fairies — or just wait for some real ones to show up!

Fab Floss

Hi, it's Flora here, but if you know anything about me, you'll know that everyone calls me Floss!

My mum, stepdad and baby brother have all popped off to Australia for six l-o-n-g months, but I got to stay behind with my lovely dad, Charlie!

We're going to spend the summer touring the countryside with all our friends at the fairground, and I get to help out!

I LOVE the fairground, especially my favourite carousel pony, Pearl, and tucking onto great big, fluffy clouds of pink candyfloss!

Have a go at my colour and design challenge and brilliant chip butty cake bake in the next few pages — I'm definitely going to!

Ever wondered what the fates have in store for you?
My fairground destiny cards will reveal all!

Love from,
Floss x

My Favourite Things!

Unscramble the letters to discover three things I like!

 AUSSN   **IHPC UTSEITB**

 KUCLY ETH ACT

The Four Worlds

Good things about going to Australia:

✓ Sunshine
✓ Beautiful beaches
✓ Koalas
✓ Kangaroos
✓ Mum will be there

I have a big dilemma. Should I stay with Dad or go to Australia with Mum and her annoying husband, Steve (and my even more annoying baby brother, Tiger)? Mum thinks it's a great adventure and I should be dying to go, but I'm not so sure...

Australia

★ Mum
★ Steve
★ Baby brother, Tiger
★ Me????

Bad things about going to Australia:

✗ Steve will be there
✗ Tiger will be there
✗ My dad WON'T be there
✗ I'll have to go to a new school
✗ I'll miss my bestie, Rhiannon

If you were Floss, what would you choose?

☐ Stay at home   ☐ Go to Australia

Why? Write your reason here -

Rhiannon is my best friend at school. She's popular and pretty and everyone wishes she was their best friend (especially Margot!). Rhiannon can be a bit bossy - well, she mostly just tells me what to do - but I don't mind. I feel lucky that she's my bestie.

I'd quite like to be friends with Susan too, but Rhiannon doesn't like her at all. She calls her Swotty Potty and makes fun of her. I wish she wouldn't be so mean to Susan, but if I say anything Rhiannon might fall out with me...

School:

☆ Mrs Horsefield
☆ Rhiannon, my best friend
☆ Margot & Judy
☆ Susan Potts (Swotty Potty)

Do you think Rhiannon sounds like a good friend for Floss?

Yes ☐
No ☐

If you were Floss, would you be friends with Susan? Write about why you made your decision -

I love the fairground, especially the carousel! Pearl is my favourite horse - she's white and has a beautiful magenta mane. I wish my hair was that colour!

And Rose the candyfloss lady is kind and lovely. She always chats to me and dad, and her pink cosy, rosy caravan is so gorgeous. She can tell fortunes too and says my luck is about to change. I do hope so...

Fairground

☆ Rose ☆ Pearl
☆ Saul ☆ Ella
☆ Liz's Lucky Darts

Throw a lucky dart to find a lucky charm for Floss. Close your eyes and hover your finger over these symbols. Count to 10, point to the page then open your eyes to reveal your choice.

What Happens Next?
Have you read Candyfloss? What do you think happens to Floss? Try writing the next chapter of her story.

My dad makes the best chip butties ever, but everyone wants wraps and sandwiches and pizza now. So things aren't going so well and his café is looking a bit worse for wear. He has hardly any customers apart from his regulars Billy the Chip, Old Ron and Miss Davis.

Dad tries his best to make everything seem okay, but I know times are hard and I can't help worrying...

Charlie's Café:

☆ My dad
☆ Billy the Chip
☆ Old Ron
☆ Miss Davis
☆ Lucky the cat

Floss's life has changed a lot since her mum and dad split up. Imagine you're a famous magazine Agony Aunt and she's written to you with her problem. What advice would you give to help ease Floss's worries?

Charlie's Chip Butty Cake!

Make Floss's dad's famous chip butty... out of cake!

You'll need:

- Ready-to-roll icing
- Brown food colouring (use orange/red + green mixed together if you can't find brown!)
- A Victoria sponge (shop-bought is fine!)
- A madeira cake (shop-bought is fine!)
- Red food colouring
- Icing sugar

To make:

1. Colour the ready-to-roll icing a light brown using the brown food colouring. Roll it out in a circle shape, then place one layer of the Victoria sponge in the middle. Fold the icing over the cake as shown, smoothing the edges as you go. Repeat for the second layer of the sponge cake.

2. Slice the madeira cake into chip-sized strips like this. Trim the ends of them lightly to make them look more chip-like.

3. Start layering the chips on the bottom layer of the Victoria sponge. Keep them to the front half of the surface and stack them up criss-crossing over each other. Use blobs of water icing to help stick the chips to each other, if needed!

4. Place the other half of the Victoria sponge on top of the chips — it should sit slightly tilted and make it look like the chips are bursting out of the bun! Sprinkle a little icing sugar on top of the cake to look like flour on the bun.

5. You can add some ketchup to the chips by mixing up some red water icing and splodging it over the cake — yum!

Fairground Destiny Cards!

CANDYFLOSS

PERSONALITY PREDICTION: Glamorous, arty and exciting!

COSMIC COLOUR: Scarlet

LUCKY NUMBER: 7

LUCKY LETTER: E

JOB DESTINY: Fashion designer

FRIEND FUTURE: A summer surprise will bring a new friend!

FAIRGROUND FORTUNE TELLER: The stars point to yes!

TOFFEE APPLE

PERSONALITY PREDICTION: Sensitive, sweet and bubbly!

COSMIC COLOUR: Caramel

LUCKY NUMBER: 18

LUCKY LETTER: G

JOB DESTINY: Pop star

FRIEND FUTURE: A fun makeover party leads to a new you!

FAIRGROUND FORTUNE TELLER: It doesn't look likely...

ICE CREAM

PERSONALITY PREDICTION: Truthful, outgoing and protective!

COSMIC COLOUR: Navy blue

LUCKY NUMBER: 31

LUCKY LETTER: N

JOB DESTINY: Policewoman

FRIEND FUTURE: Uh-oh, we see some trouble for you two...

FAIRGROUND FORTUNE TELLER: Only time will tell, I'm afraid...

FERRIS WHEEL

PERSONALITY PREDICTION: Funny, friendly and a great listener

COSMIC COLOUR: Gold

LUCKY NUMBER: 23

LUCKY LETTER: Y

JOB DESTINY: Author

FRIEND FUTURE: Solving your bestie's problem will give you confidence...

FAIRGROUND FORTUNE TELLER: Looks like a definite 'yes'!

CAROUSEL

PERSONALITY PREDICTION: Fun, loyal and determined!

COSMIC COLOUR: Violet

LUCKY NUMBER: 1

LUCKY LETTER: A

JOB DESTINY: Athlete

FRIEND FUTURE: Having a sleepover is great for sharing secrets...

FAIRGROUND FORTUNE TELLER: This isn't going to happen...

ROLLERCOASTER

PERSONALITY PREDICTION: Passionate, artistic and unique!

COSMIC COLOUR: Lemon yellow

LUCKY NUMBER: 13

LUCKY LETTER: M

JOB DESTINY: Artist

FRIEND FUTURE: One of your friends is feeling left out... try to find out why

FAIRGROUND FORTUNE TELLER: The signs are looking good...

HOW TO PLAY!

○ Carefully cut out the cards.
○ Pop them into a bag.
○ Everyone takes turns to pull out a card.
○ Read the card to reveal your fairground fortune!

CUDDLY TOY

PERSONALITY PREDICTION: Caring, supportive and generous!

COSMIC COLOUR: Emerald green

LUCKY NUMBER: 8

LUCKY LETTER: L

JOB DESTINY: Doctor

FRIEND FUTURE: Joining a new club can be scary, so ask your BFF to come along, too

FAIRGROUND FORTUNE TELLER: There is a strong possibility this will happen

GHOST TRAIN

PERSONALITY PREDICTION: Intelligent, daring and dedicated!

COSMIC COLOUR: Silver

LUCKY NUMBER: 5

LUCKY LETTER: T

JOB DESTINY: Scientist

FRIEND FUTURE: Some problems need a second opinion — ask a friend for advice

FAIRGROUND FORTUNE TELLER: The answer is no.

HELTER SKELTER

PERSONALITY PREDICTION: Creative, confident and imaginative!

COSMIC COLOUR: Baby blue

LUCKY NUMBER: 22

LUCKY LETTER: C

JOB DESTINY: Actress

FRIEND FUTURE: Getting together to talk it all over makes everything go back to normal

FAIRGROUND FORTUNE TELLER: There is no doubt — this will happen!

FUN HOUSE

PERSONALITY PREDICTION: Fun-loving, upbeat and caring!

COSMIC COLOUR: Hot pink

LUCKY NUMBER: 2

LUCKY LETTER: W

JOB DESTINY: Teacher

FRIEND FUTURE: Giving THAT girl a second chance may end in a pleasant surprise...

FAIRGROUND FORTUNE TELLER: The chances of this are looking doubtful.

Ask The Fairground Fortune Teller!

How to play:

☆ Write the numbers 1-10 on little pieces of paper, fold them up and put them in a bowl.

☆ Take turns to pull a number from the bowl (remember to close your eyes, when it's your turn!).

☆ Match your number to the questions below and concentrate hard on the question.

☆ Close your eyes and pick one of the fairground cards to find out what prediction the fortune teller has made!

1. Will I ever be a millionaire?
2. Will I ever be famous?
3. Should I give myself a makeover?
4. Will I go to university?
5. Should I organise a summer party?
6. Will I meet my favourite celebrity?
7. Will I ever travel the world?
8. Should I get a daring new hairstyle?
9. Will I see my favourite band play live?
10. Will I be a successful author like Jacky?

Kitty & Lucy

Hello, I'm Lucy Locket! And I'm Kitty Fisher!
And together we are... the Runaway Girls!
We met on the streets of Victorian London and
we've had quite the adventure! From toiling away
in a workhouse, to performing at the circus!
Perhaps you'd like to join us on our journey?
Well, you're in luck... in the next few pages,
we'll teach you how to create your very own
Victorian character!
We'll teach you how to sketch US! Perhaps
you'll sketch us on a whole new adventure?
Are you ready? We are! Turn the page to begin!

Very Victorian!

Can you guess which of these
Victorian facts are true or false?

1. The Victorian Era
   was named after
   King Victor!

2. Many people
   consumed poison
   called arsenic!

3. Queen Victoria's
   real name wasn't
   actual Victoria... it
   was Alexandrina!

4. Televisions were
   very popular in
   Victorian times!

5. Queen Victoria
   is the UK's
   longest reigning
   monarch!

Answers

1. False, 2. True
3. True, 4. False
5. False — Queen
Elizabeth II
overtook her!

Kitty & Lucy's Character Creator!

Create your own Victorian!

Choose A Character!

Roll a dice to find your Victorian character.

1. Henry, ragamuffin boy
2. Charles Junior, heir to a vast fortune
3. Suzie Brown, servant to a retired admiral
4. Minnie, mother to nine hungry children
5. Little Harriet, a runaway orphan
6. Madame Lucille, psychic extraordinaire

Design your Victorian!

What does your character look like? Are they clean and well-presented, or dirty-faced and wearing ragged clothes? Can they afford to wear expensive jewellery and silk gloves, or have they barely enough money for shoes?

Draw your character here!

Pick A Personality!

Think about your character. How would their lifestyle affect their personality. Perhaps they'll be the opposite — a happy-go-lucky orphan or a sad, frightened, rich girl, like Kitty and Lucy? Choose three character traits to help build up your character's personality.

Hard-working ☐

Determined ☐

Lazy ☐

Greedy ☐

Deceitful ☐

Kind-hearted ☐

Desperate ☐

Happy-go-lucky ☐

Spoilt ☐

Mean-spirited ☐

Decide Their Destiny!

What will become of your character? Cut off the DESTINY letters at the bottom of the page, put them in a bowl and pick one out to find your character's fate!

D A visit to the circus changes their lives forever

E The police investigate a suspicious will and uncover a terrible secret

N Hetty Feather takes them under her wing

I A chance encounter with a wealthy lady leads to great things

S A special invitation arrives from Queen Victoria herself

Y A tragic accident turns their lives upside down

T A strong friendship is formed that will last a lifetime

Now try writing an exciting story based on your Victorian character!

D E S T I N Y

How To Draw
Kitty & Lucy!

Sketch here!

Copy one box at a time!

KITTY

LUCY

Use a gold metallic pen to make Kitty's braiding really stand out!

Imagine if Lucy wore Kitty's outfit instead!

Sketch here!

Bad Girls!

Hi! We're Tanya and Mandy, and welcome to the most colourful section of this book! We're best friends, even though we are total opposites. Like peanut butter and jam, ice cream and French fries, or colourful odd socks — we go together just fine! Do you have any strange food combinations you like to eat together?

Write them below!

Love, Tanya and Mandy xx

★★ My weird food combo! ★★
& ....

MANDY OR TANYA?

Can you match each fact up with the character it's about?

. I stole a green velvet hairband from Mr and Mrs Patel.
Mandy ☐ Tanya ☐

2. I was bullied by Kim, Melanie and Sarah at school.
Mandy ☐ Tanya ☐

I like to collect toy monkeys.
andy ☐ Tanya ☐

4. I was arrested for stealing a posh sweatshirt.
Mandy ☐ Tanya ☐

5. I'm dyslexic!
Mandy ☐ Tanya ☐

. I created an imaginary character called Miranda Rainbow.
Mandy ☐ Tanya ☐

7. I have a sister called Carmel.
Mandy ☐ Tanya ☐

How many did you score?

☐/7

ANSWERS- 1.Tanya, 2.Mandy, 3.Mandy, 4.Tanya, 5.Tanya, 6.Mandy, 7.Tanya

This colour makes me happy...

The colour of my favourite top...

If I was a mermaid, my tail would be...

The colour of my pencil case...

I find this colour very calming...

I could wear this colour all day, every day...

BLUE
You're a sensitive soul with a heart of gold. Friends can trust you with their biggest secrets and everyone knows you give the best hugs!

INDIGO
You have the wow factor! No matter where you go, you've just got to be in the spotlight because you shine like a star. Dazzling!

VIOLET
You have many positive traits but your main strength is your absolute honesty and loyalty. That's what makes you such a good friend!

89

COLOUR MADE EASY

Bring your artwork to life with our top colour tips...

Mixing Colours

We show you how to mix a whole rainbow of colours using just yellow, blue and red!

Primary Colours

The three colours in the centre of the Colour Wheel are called Primary Colours. They are all you need to create every other colour, except white and black.

Secondary Colours

These colours are shown on the second ring of the Colour Wheel. They can be made by simply mixing a Primary Colour with the colour directly beside it.

For example:

Blue + yellow = green

Opal's Tip!

Paints are best for mixing new colours, but chalks and pastels also work well!

Tones

These are all the colours on the third ring of the wheel. They are created by mixing a Secondary Colour with a Primary Colour. Experiment with different amounts of colours to mix various tones.

For example:

A lot of red + a little purple = magenta

A little red + a lot of purple = indigo

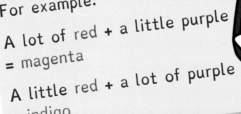

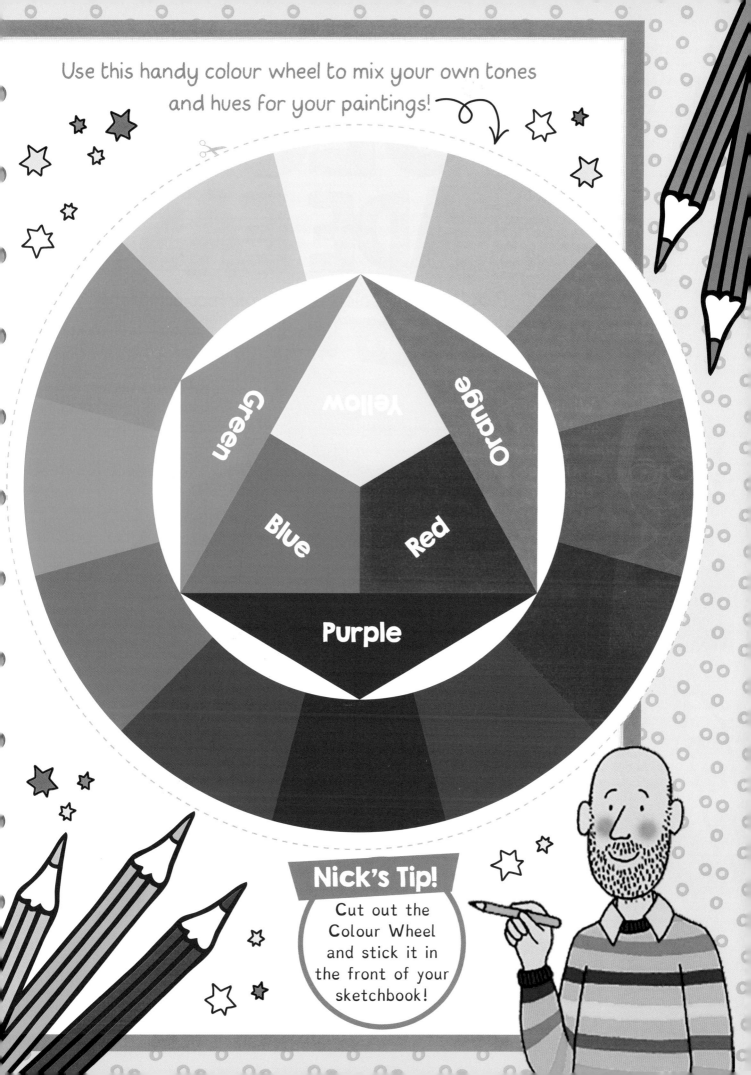

Use this handy colour wheel to mix your own tones and hues for your paintings!

Green

Yellow

Orange

Blue

Red

Purple

Nick's Tip!

Cut out the Colour Wheel and stick it in the front of your sketchbook!

COLOUR MADE EASY

Pick the right colours for a perfect picture!

Hot & Cold Colours

What do you think of when you look at the hot colours?

Let's draw an imaginary line through the centre of the Colour Wheel, like below:

....
....
....

These colours are the hot colours. They make you feel all warm and cosy inside. Hot colours are perfect for creating:

- A glorious sunset
- Scorching desert landscape
- Summer flowers

The colours on this half of the wheel are called cold colours. They have a calming effect. Cold colours work well for:

- A winter sky
- A barren icy landscape
- A crisp spring scene

Look at the cold colours again. How do they make you feel?

....
....
....

Use our top tips to make a mini masterpiece!

Use paint, pens, pencils, crayons or even chalks to colour this scene!

Nick's Tip!

An old plastic plate makes a great mixing palette!